This book is for:

....

....

For my lovely mum,
thanks for everything
~ B J

LITTLE TIGER PRE
1 The Coda Centre, 189 Munster Road, London SW6 6A
www.littletiger.co

Published in Great Britain 20

A CIP catalogue record for this book is availal
from the British Libre

Colouring for Mums to be

LTP
London

Especially For You

Growing a little person is hard work, and that's why relaxation is
essential throughout your pregnancy journey. Colouring is a wonderfully
therapeutic way of relieving everyday stresses, and the beautiful
baby-themed designs in this book will help to promote a sense of
wellbeing as you count down the days to your special new arrival.

Pop it in your handbag ready for those hospital appointments,
or put your feet up at home and enjoy
a moment of colouring calm.

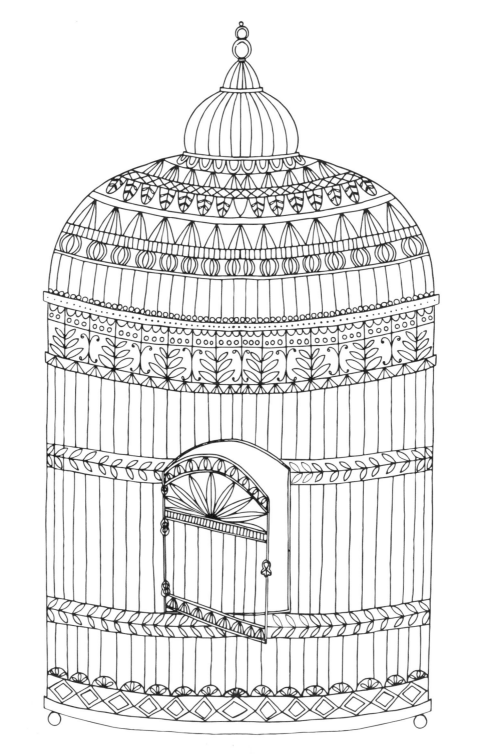

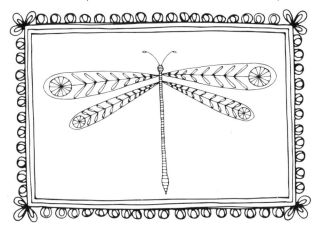

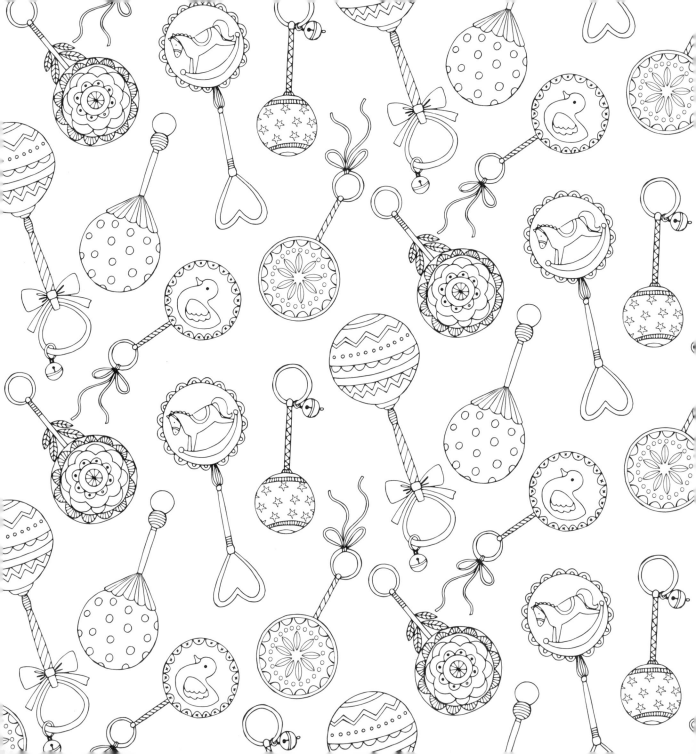

Fill this space with your own designs and daydreams.